ADVENTURES OF LOLLIPOP NUMBER **2**

Lollipop's Canada: Coast to Coast!

BY: JENNIFER CUTHBERT

PEPPERMINT PUBLISHING

Library and Archives Canada Cataloguing in Publication

Cuthbert, Jennifer, 1984-
Lollipop's Canada coast to coast : adventures of Lollipop #2
written and illustrated by Jennifer Cuthbert.

ISBN 0-9732053-1-8

1. Canada—Description and travel—Comic books, strips, etc.—Juvenile literature. I. Title.

PN6733.C88L64 2004   j741.5'971   C2004-904232-7

Printed in Canada

1 2 3 4 5 6

CONTENTS

Lollipop The Characters

PEPPERMINT TWIST

VIOLET VICKEY

CRUSHER

MISS PINK

FRASER

CAMERON

LOLLIPOP!

BRIAN

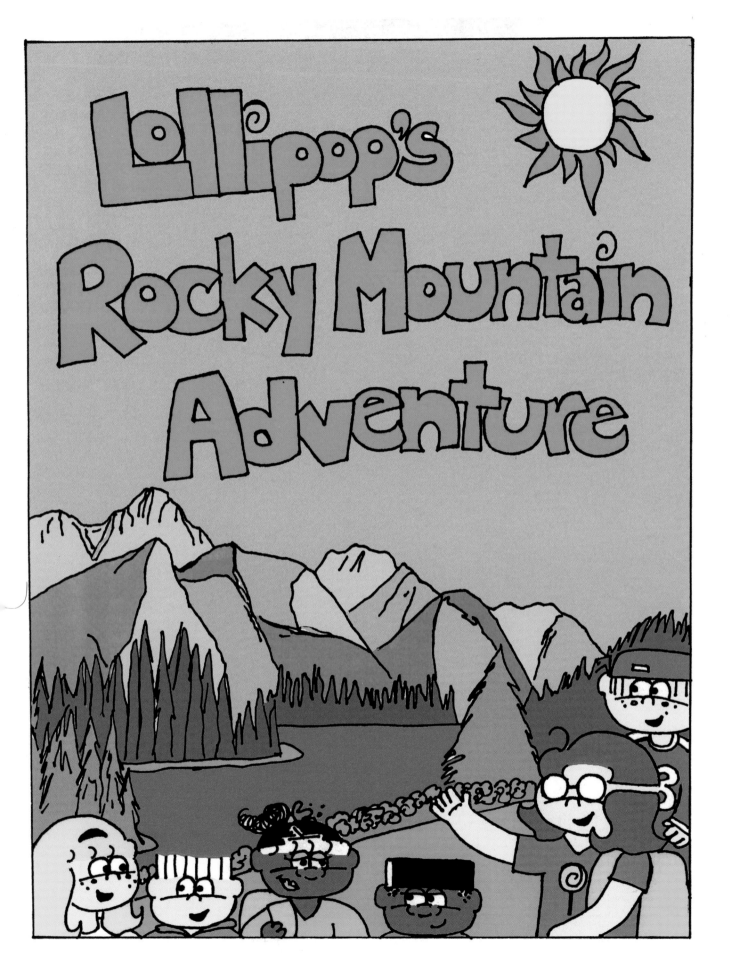

21

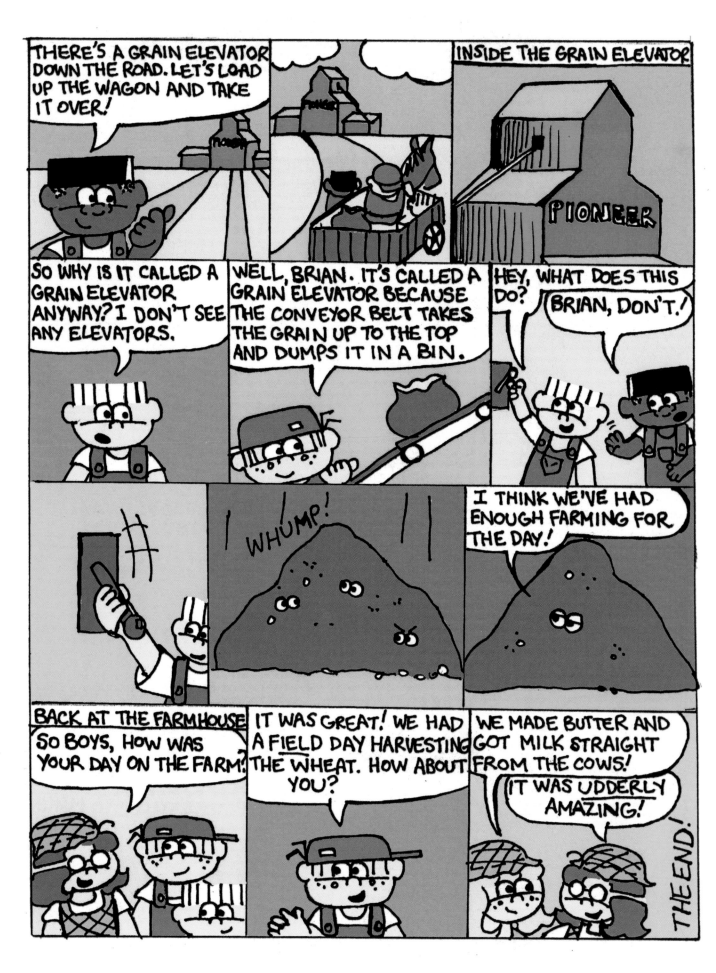

22

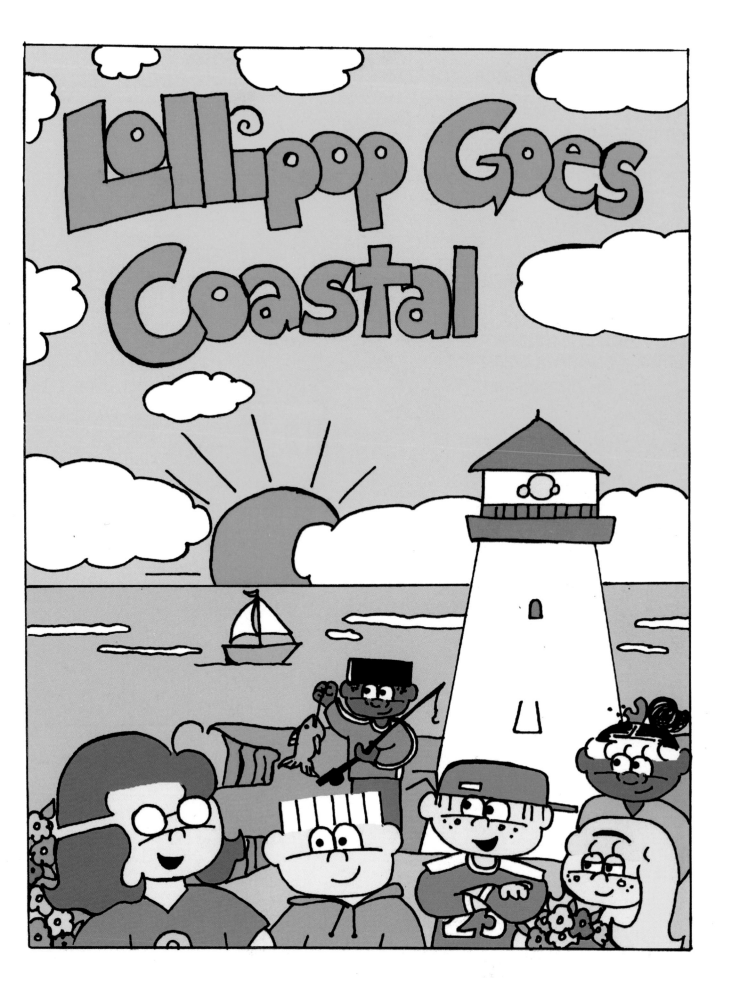

38

ABOUT THE AUTHOR

Jennifer Cuthbert is an undergraduate History student at York University in Toronto. Jennifer has been drawing and writing stories about Lollipop and her friends since the age of nine. She wrote her first book, *The Adventures of Lollipop* in 2002 and frequently visits schools to share Lollipop stories. Jennifer lives in Brampton, Ontario with her parents, brother and dog, Fraser.